You Make Me Feel So Young

Words by Mack Gordon
Music by Josef Myrow

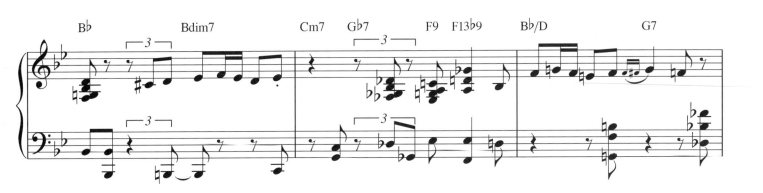

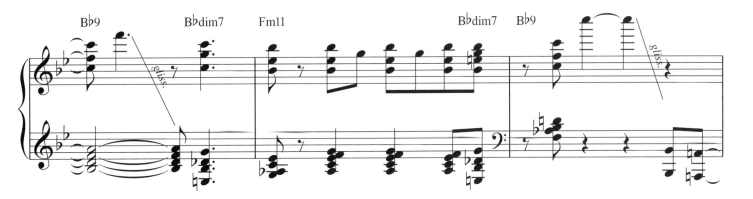

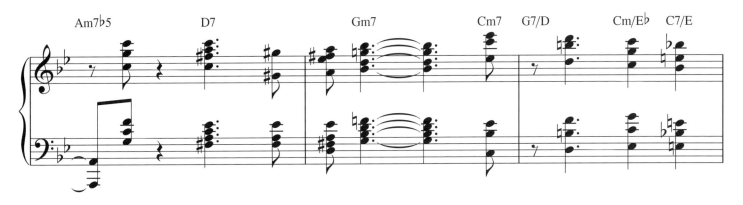

5

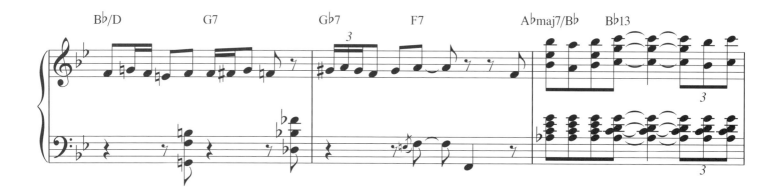

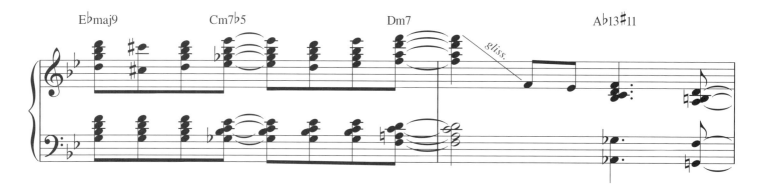

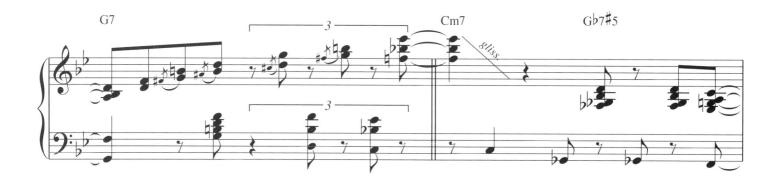

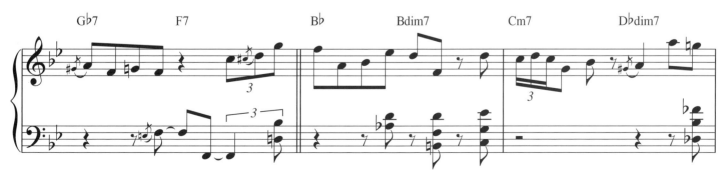

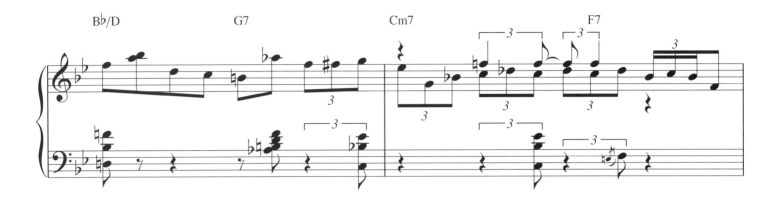

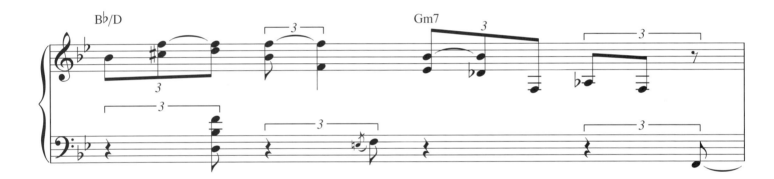

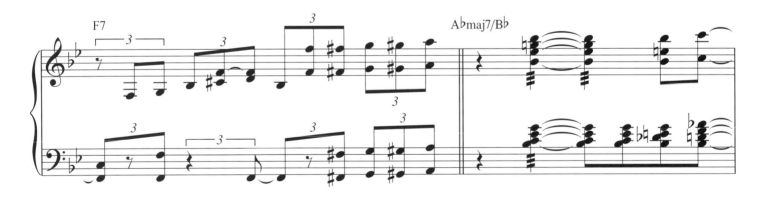

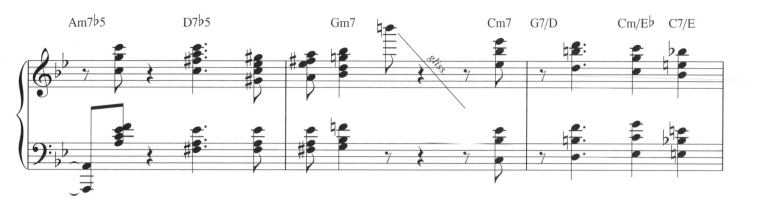

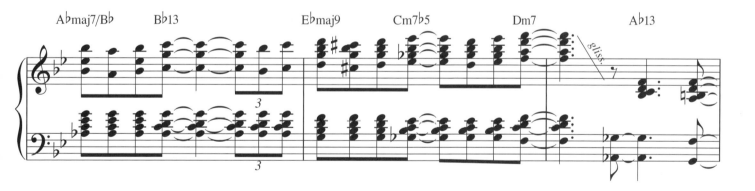

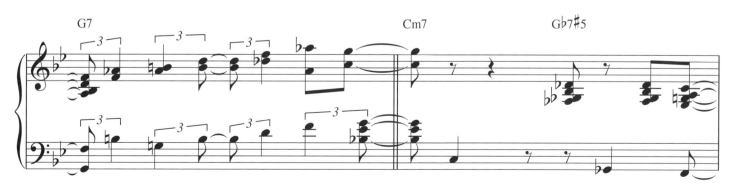

9

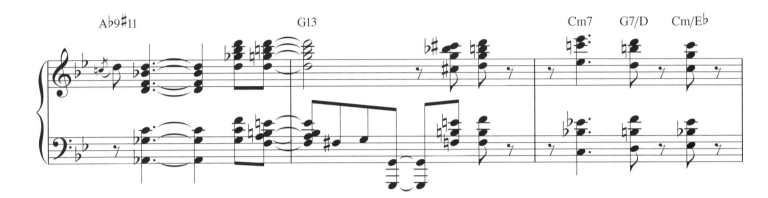

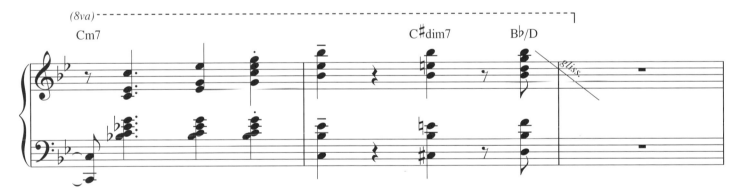

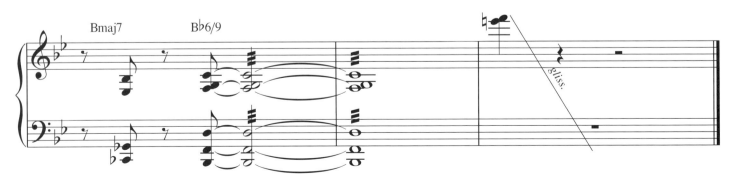

Come Dance with Me

Words by Sammy Cahn
Music by James Van Heusen

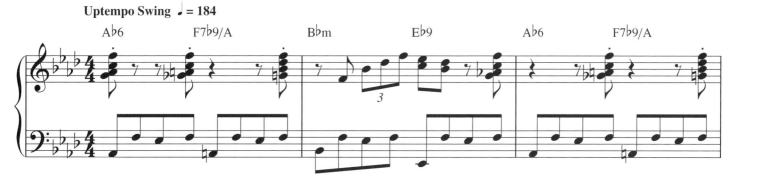

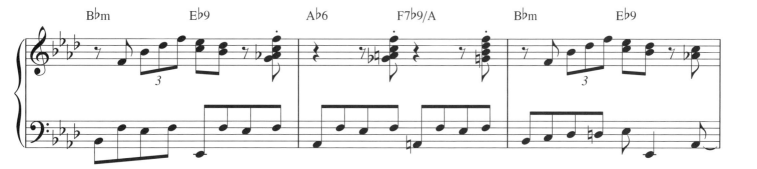

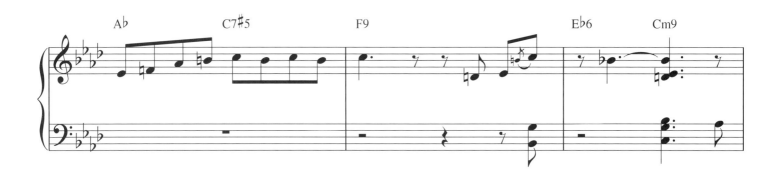

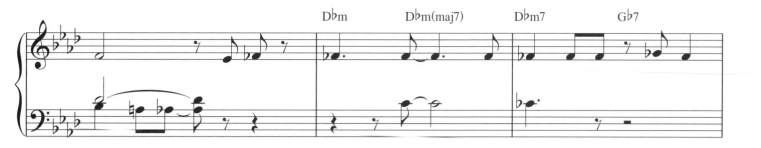

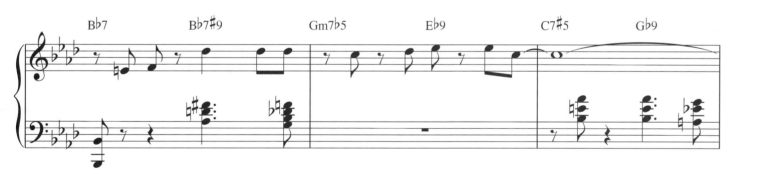

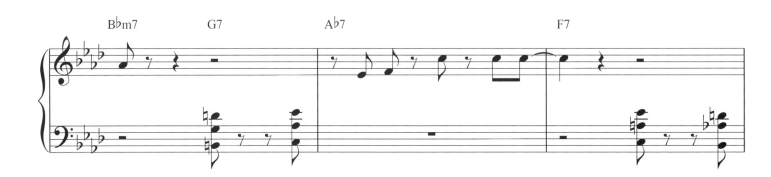

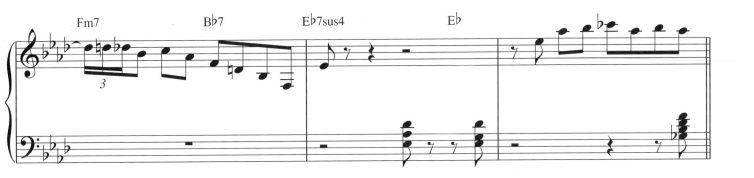

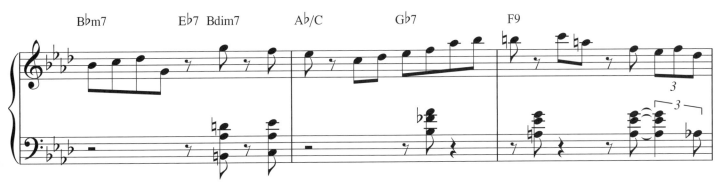

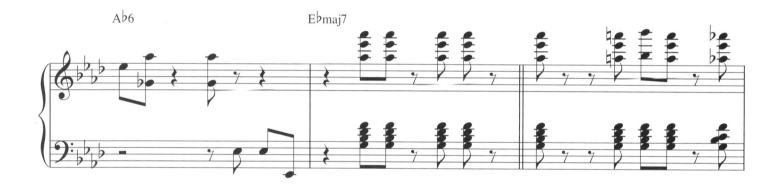

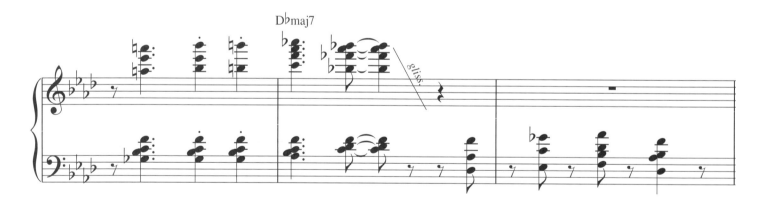

Learnin' the Blues

Words and Music by Dolores "Vicki" Silvers

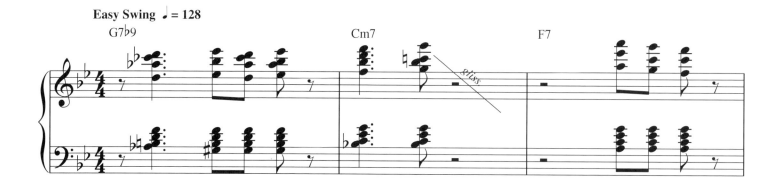

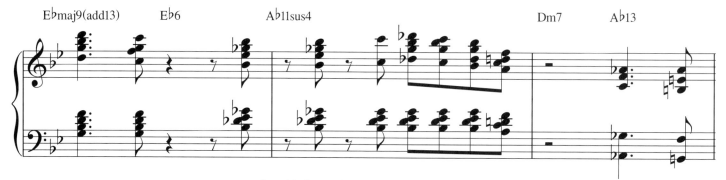

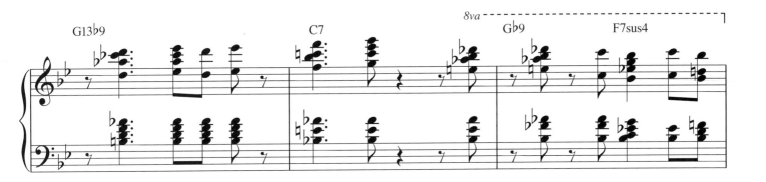

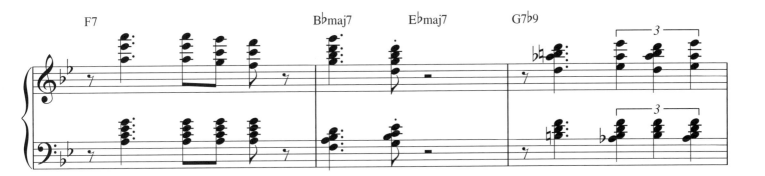

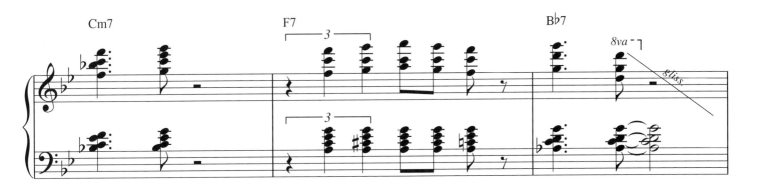

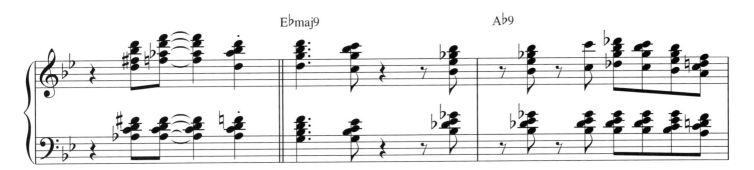

19

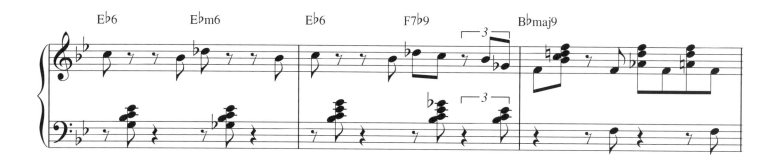

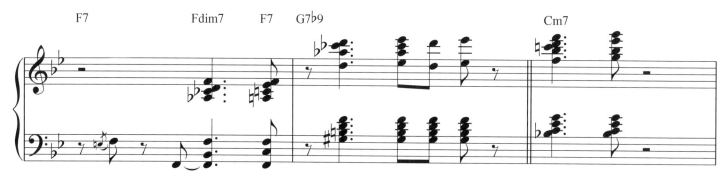

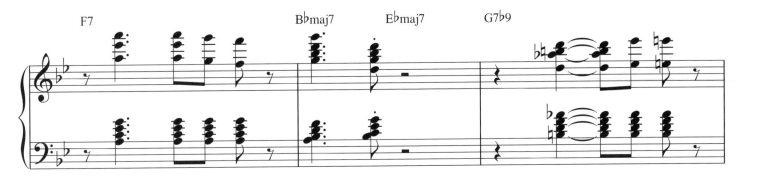

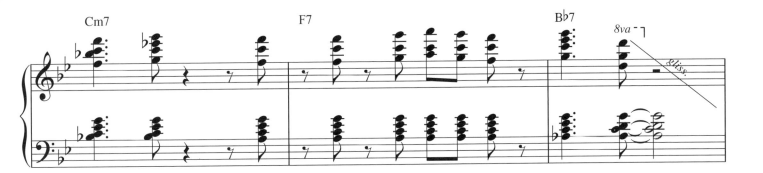

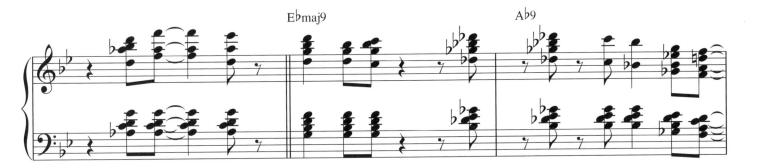

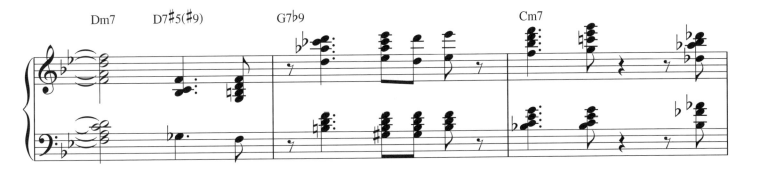

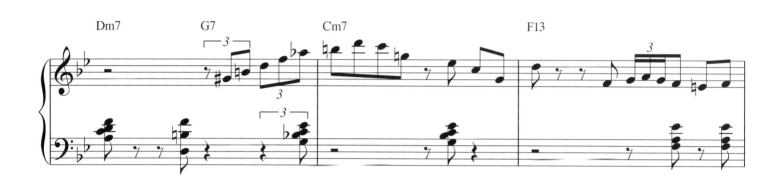

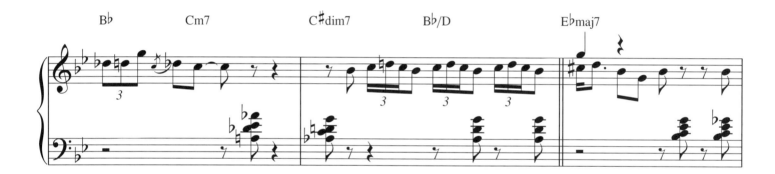

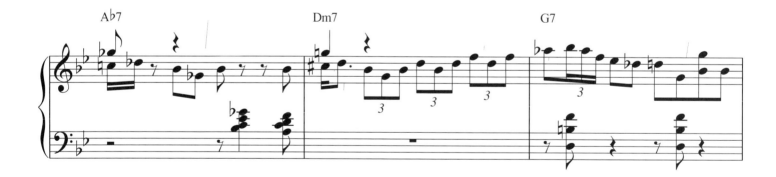

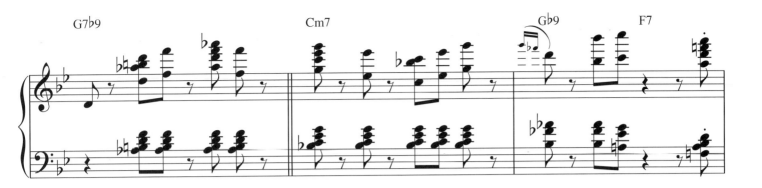

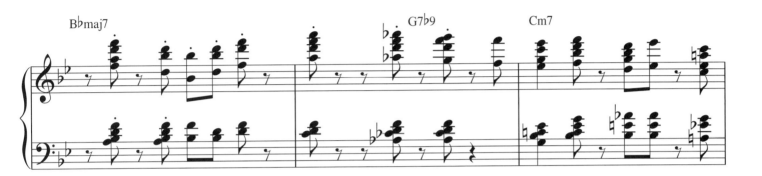

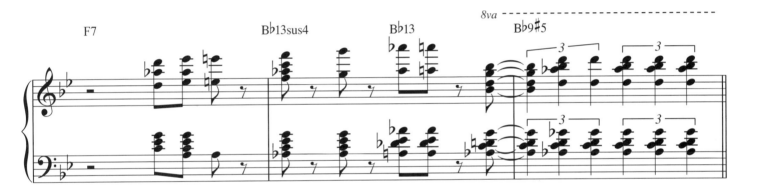

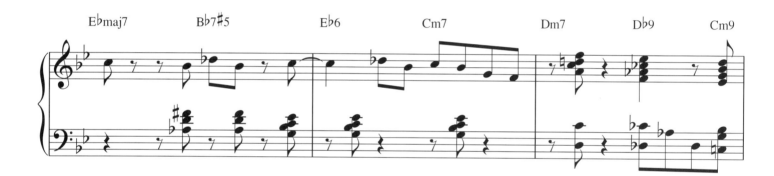

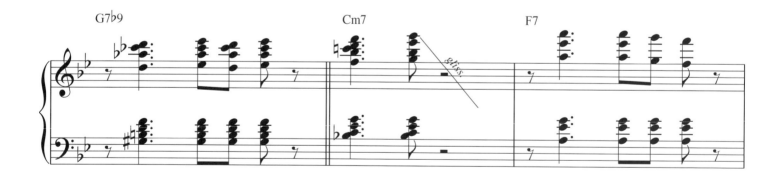

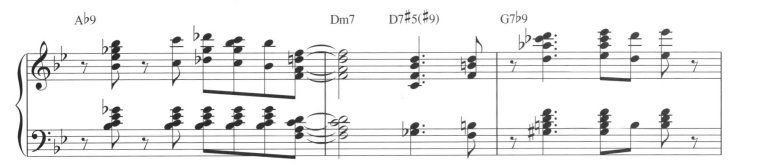

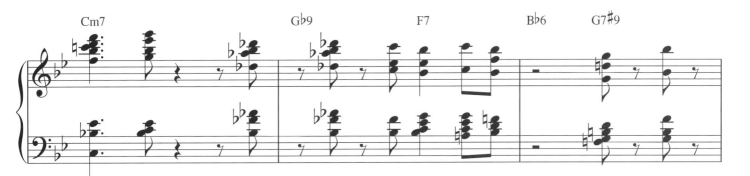

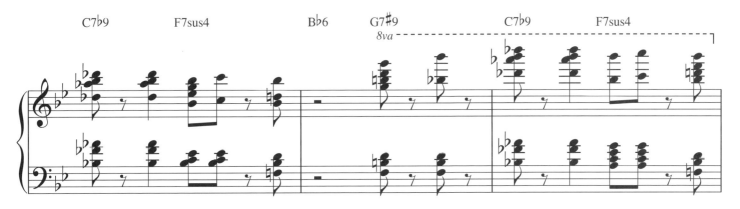

Witchcraft

Music by Cy Coleman
Lyrics by Carolyn Leigh

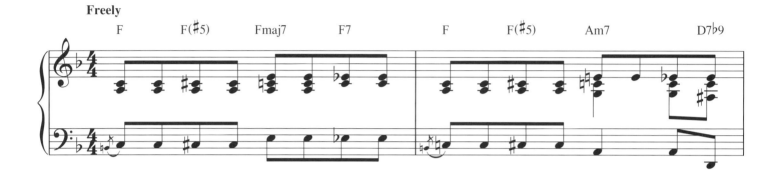

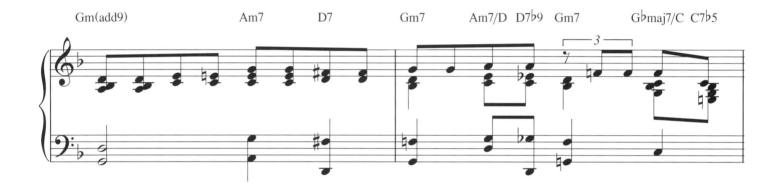

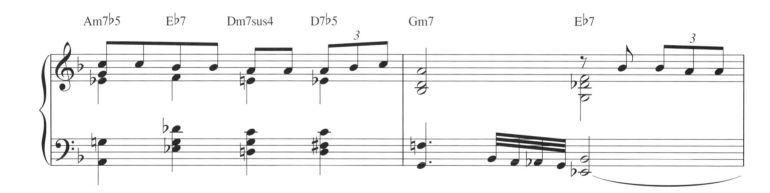

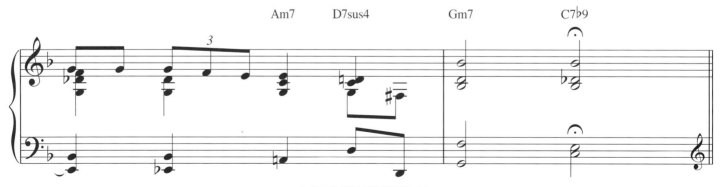

Easy Swing ♩ = 130
bass and drums enter

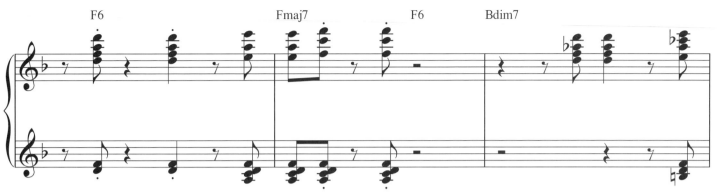

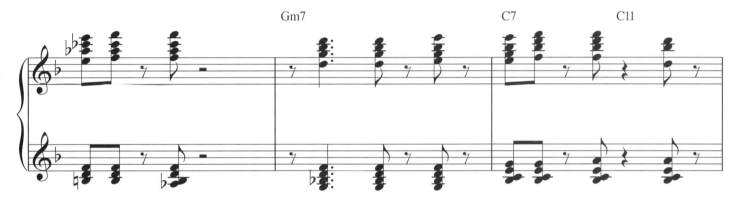

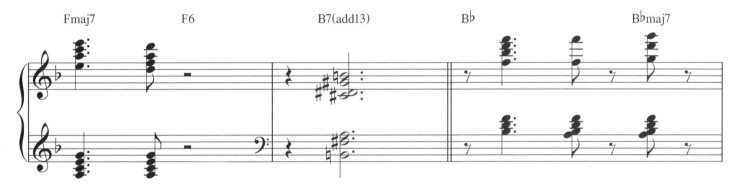

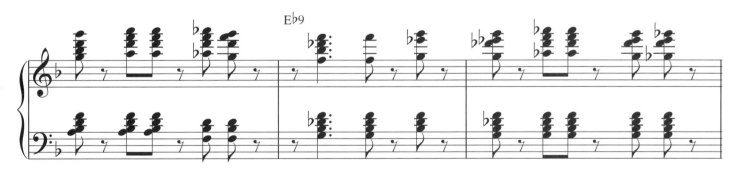

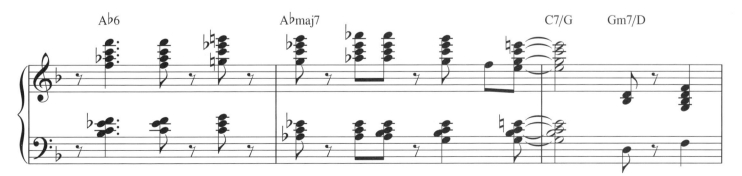

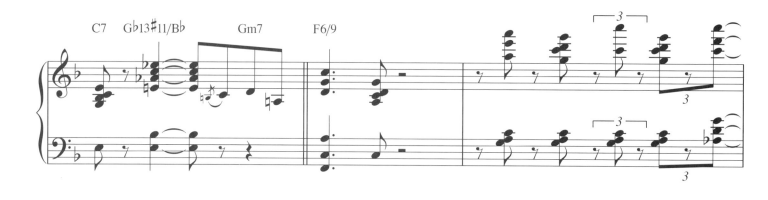

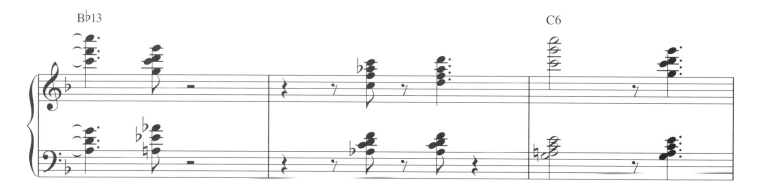

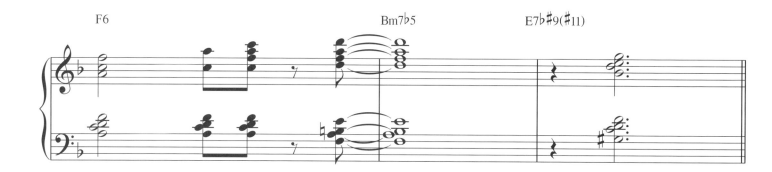

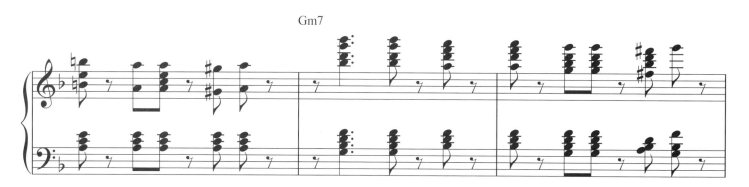

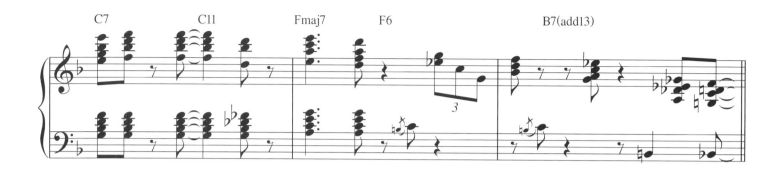

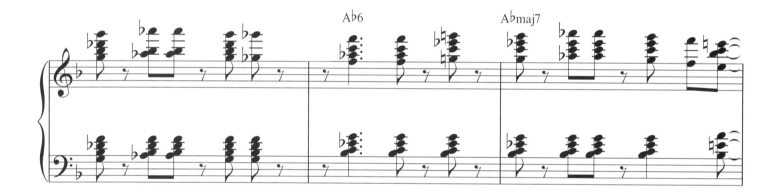

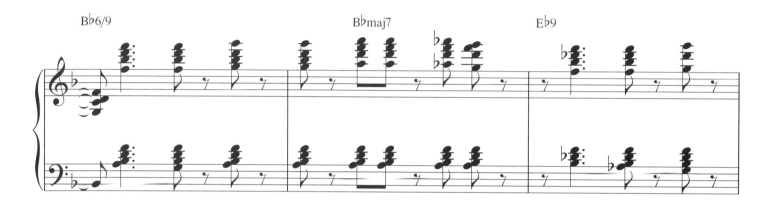

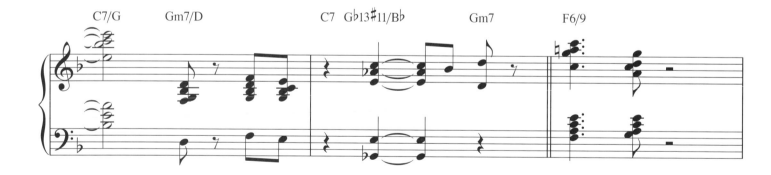

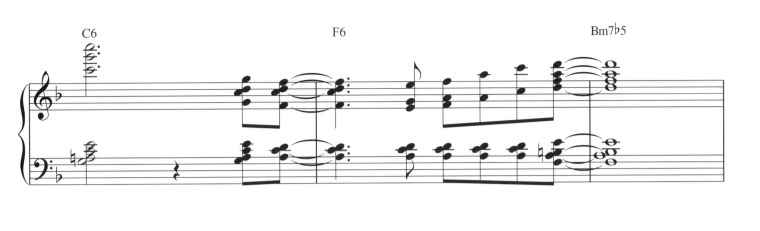

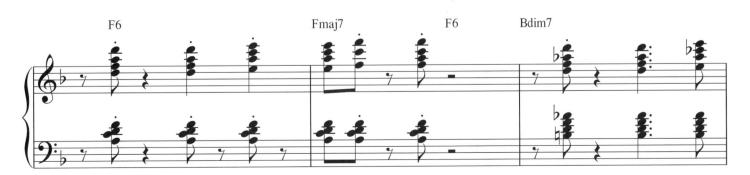

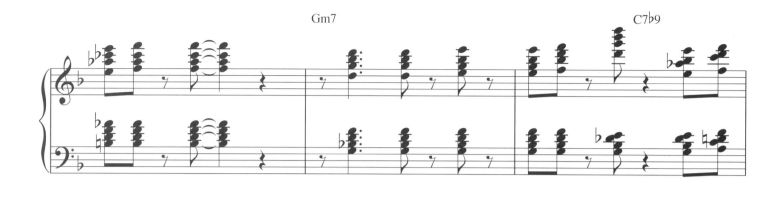

Gm7　　　　　　　　　　　　　　　　　C7♭9

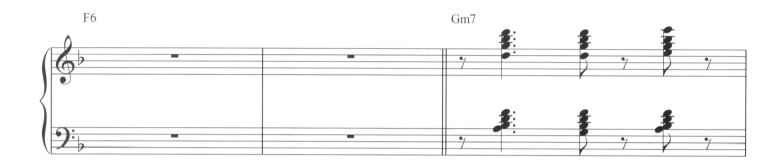

F6　　　　　　　　　　　　　　Gm7

bass fill

C7♭9　　　　　　　　F6

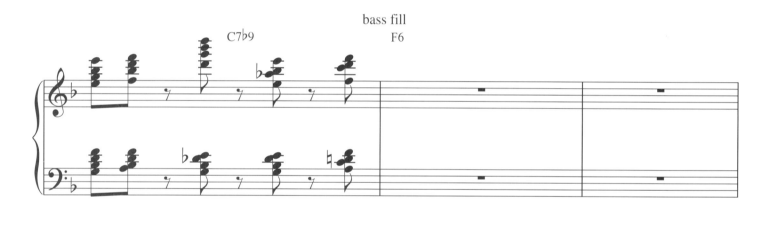

Gm7　　　　　　　　　　　　　　　　C7♭9

G♭maj7　　　　　　　　　　　　　　　Fmaj9

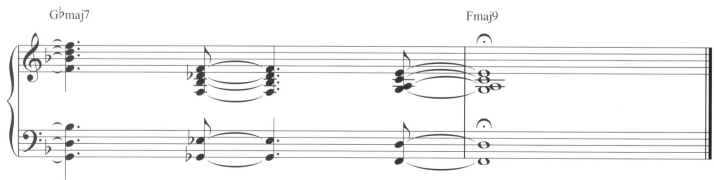

(Love Is) The Tender Trap

Words by Sammy Cahn
Music by James Van Heusen

Moderate Swing ♩ = 138

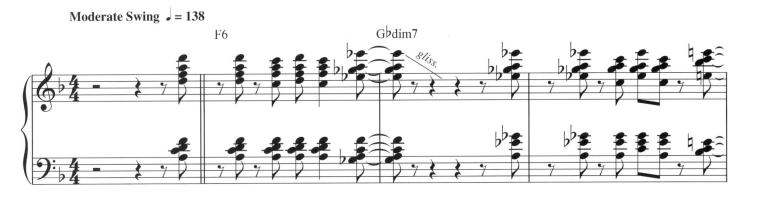

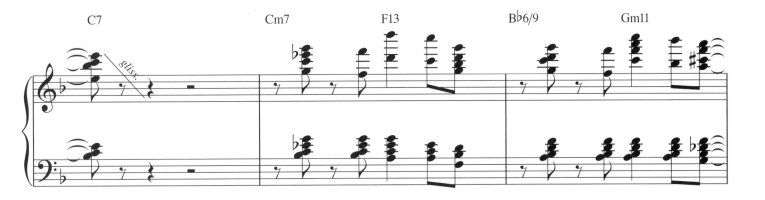

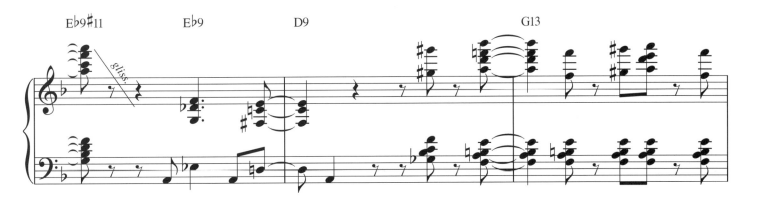

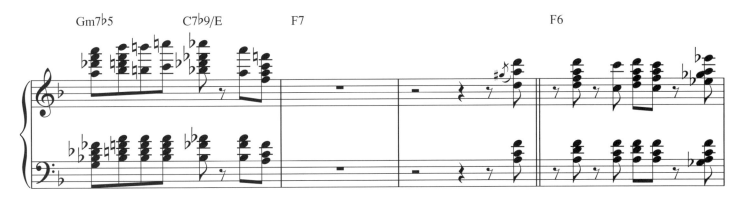

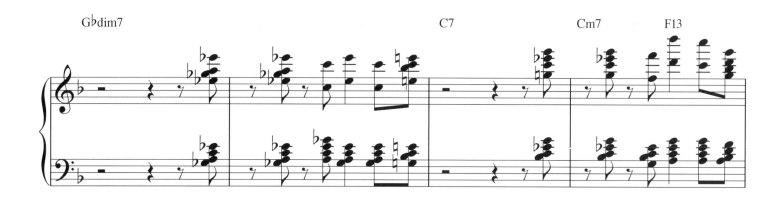

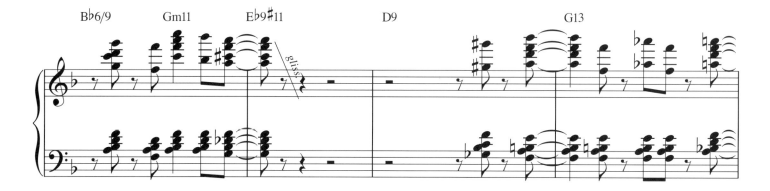

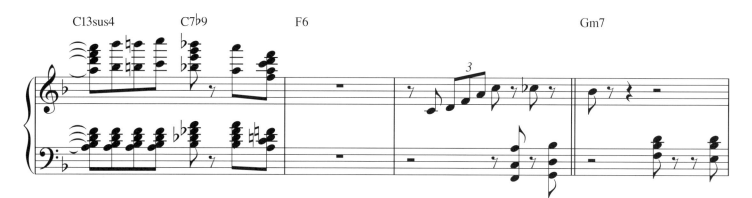

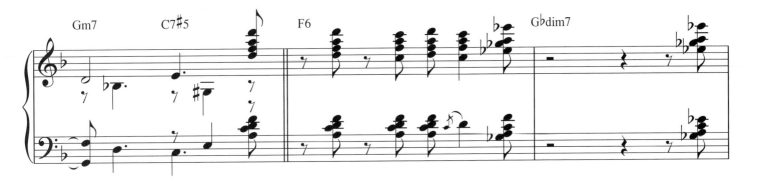

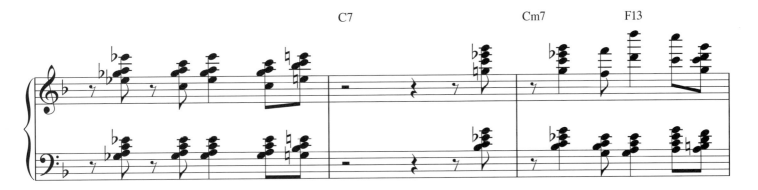

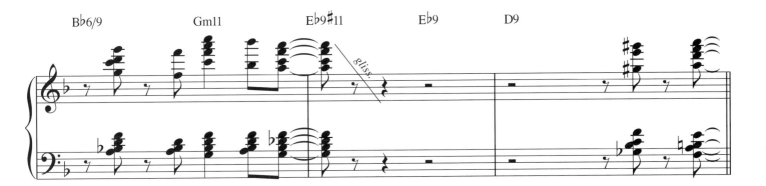

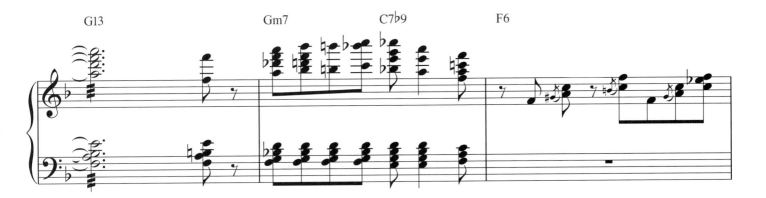

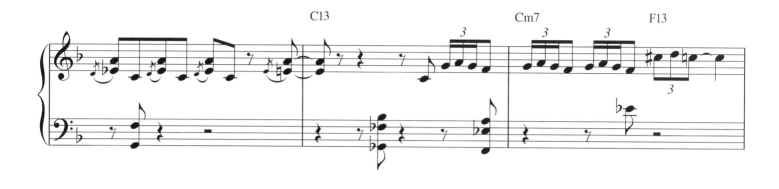

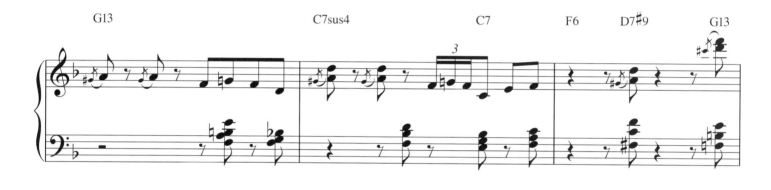

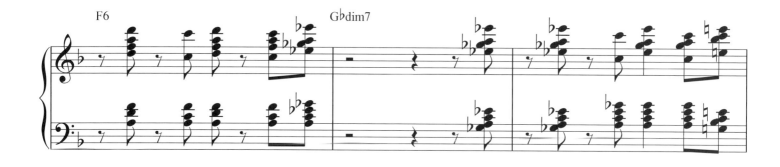

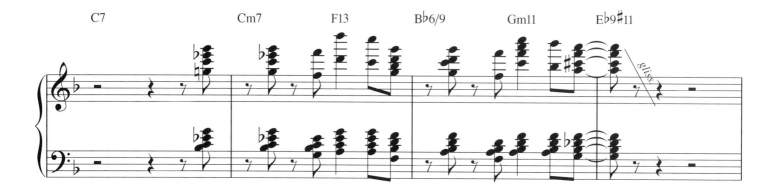

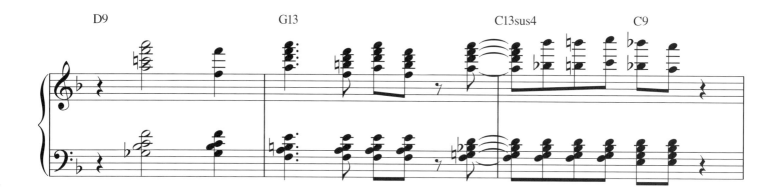

Saturday Night (Is the Loneliest Night of the Week)

Words by Sammy Cahn
Music by Jule Styne

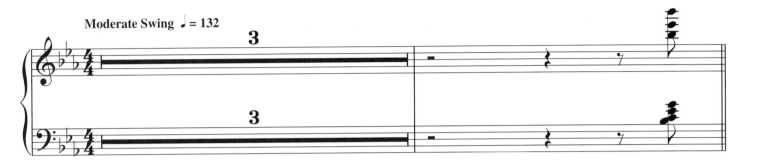

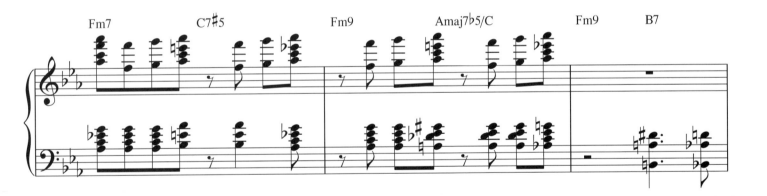

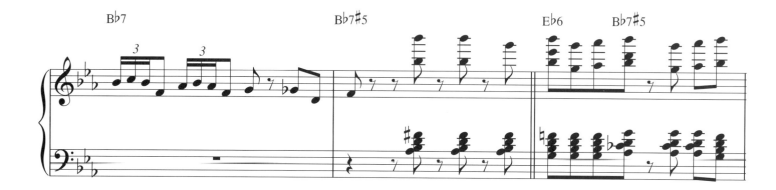

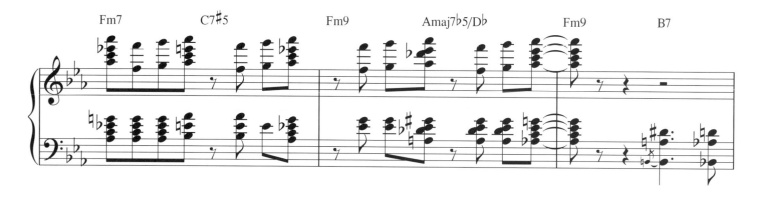

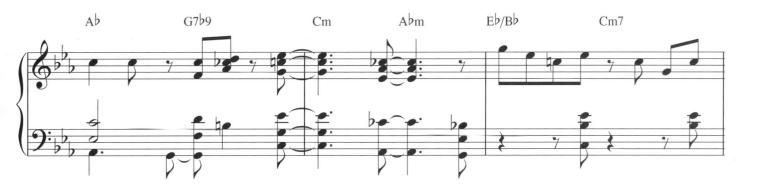

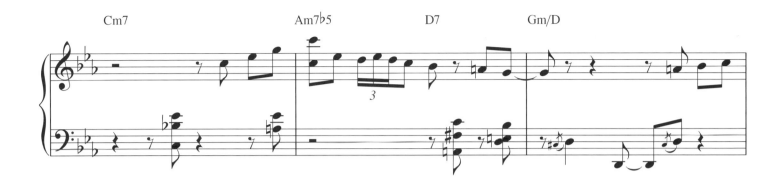

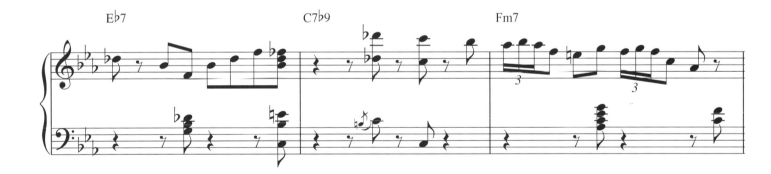

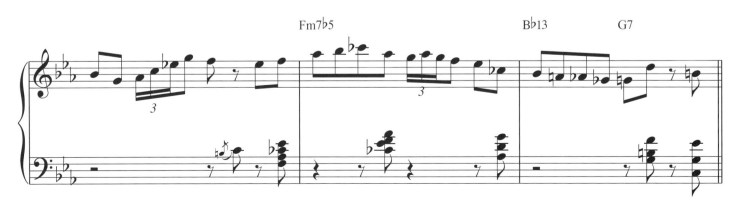

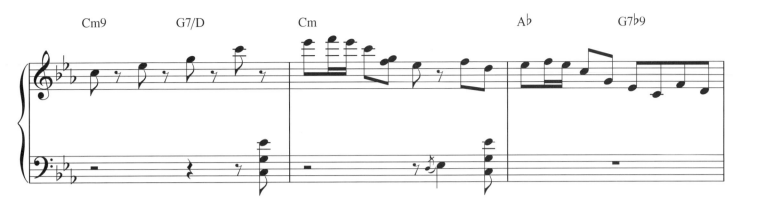

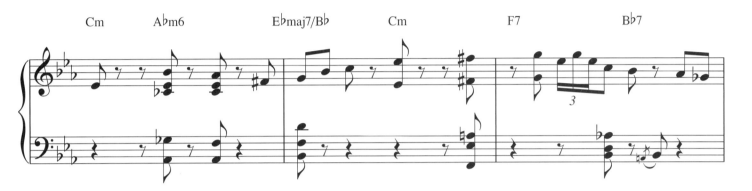

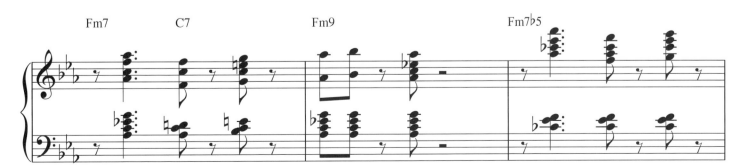

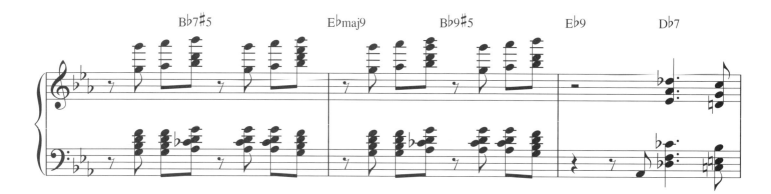

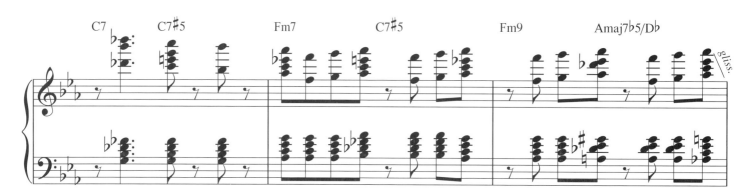

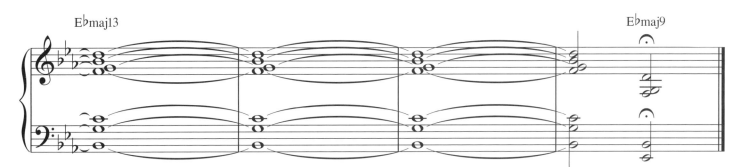

Just in Time

Words by Betty Comden and Adolph Green
Music by Jule Styne

Easy Swing ♩ = 118

drum intro

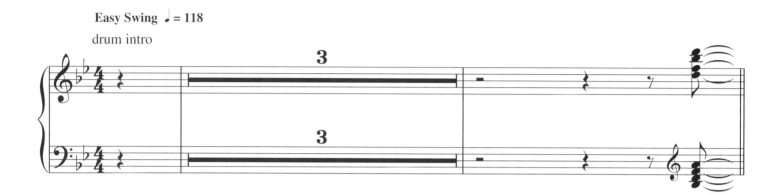

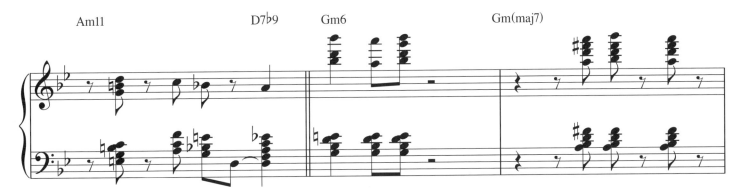

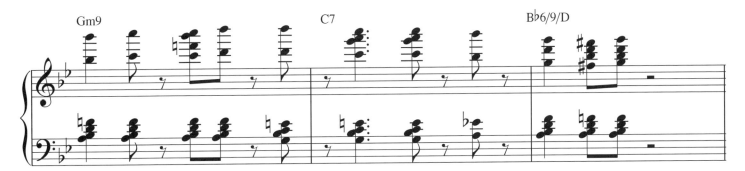

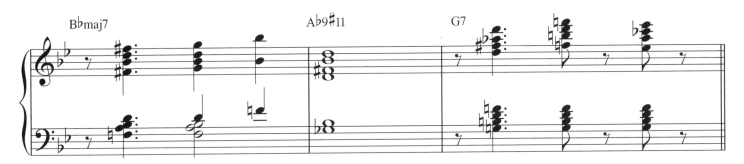

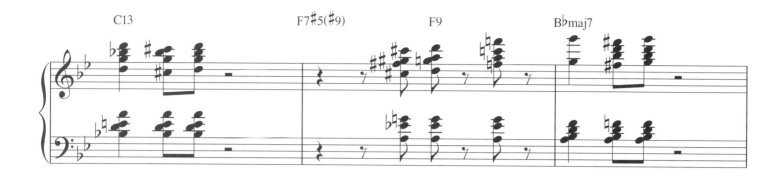

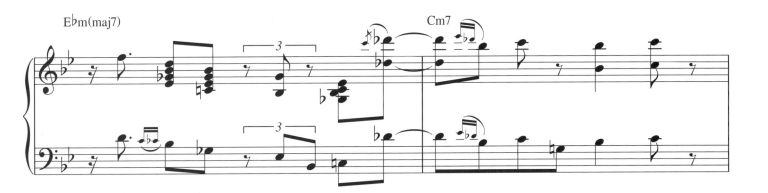

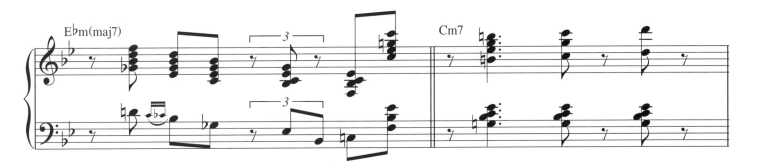

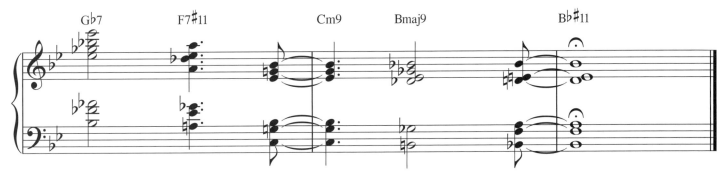

It Happened in Monterey

Words by Billy Rose
Music by Mabel Wayne

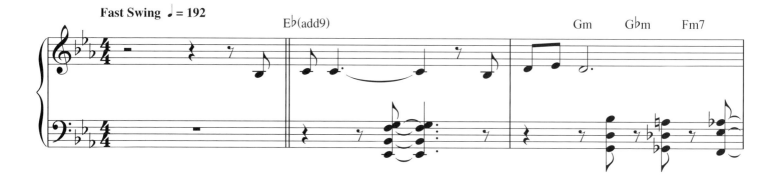

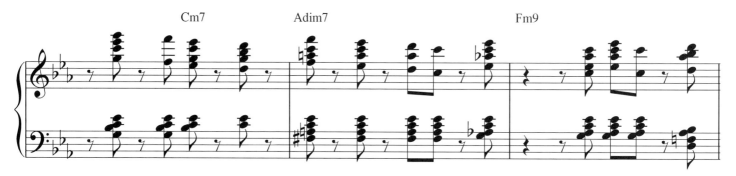

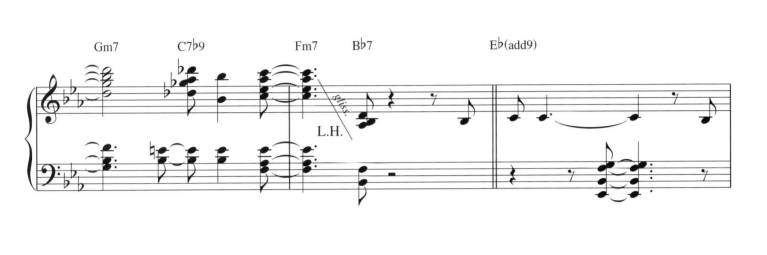

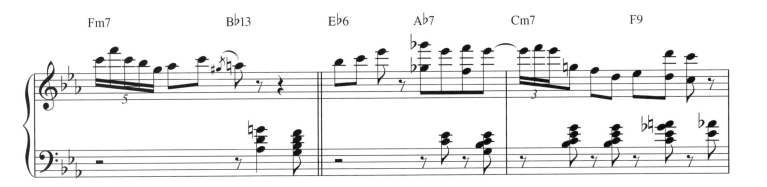

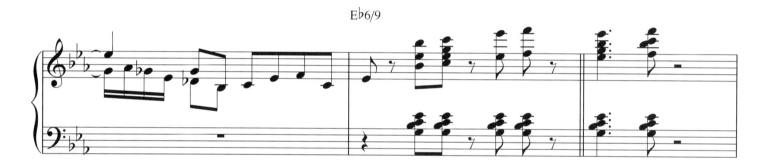

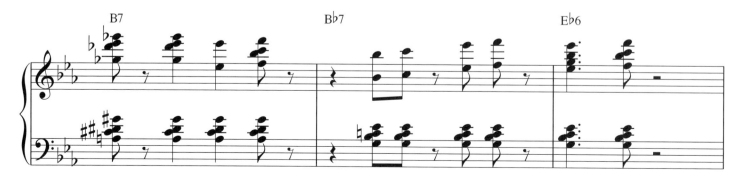

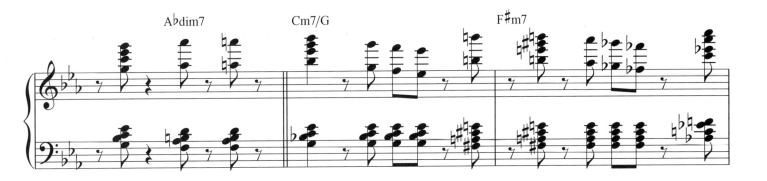

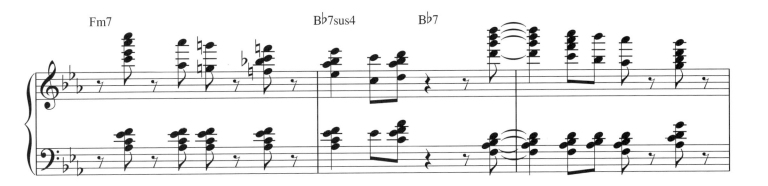

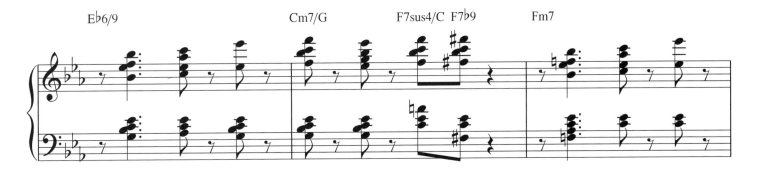

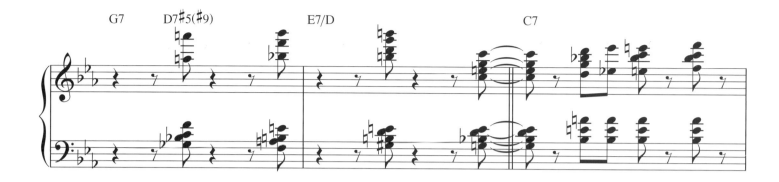

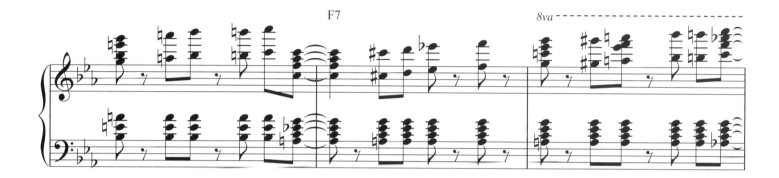

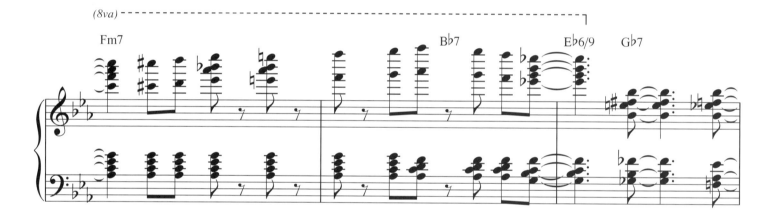

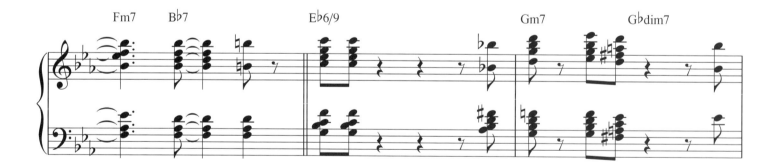

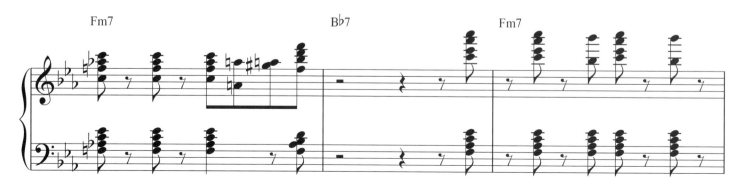

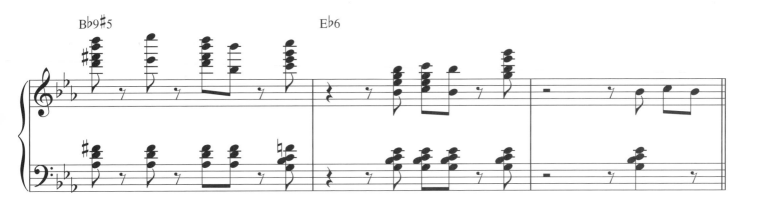

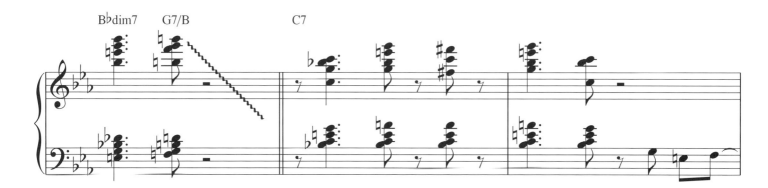

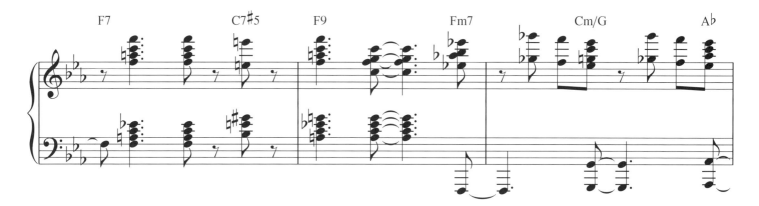

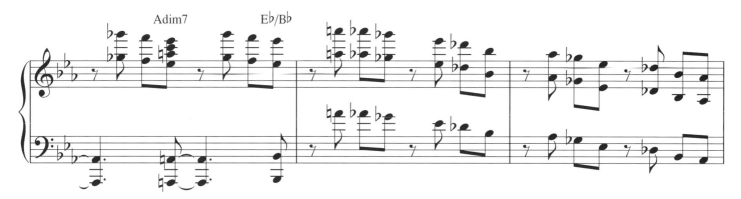

I Get a Kick Out of You

Words and Music by Cole Porter

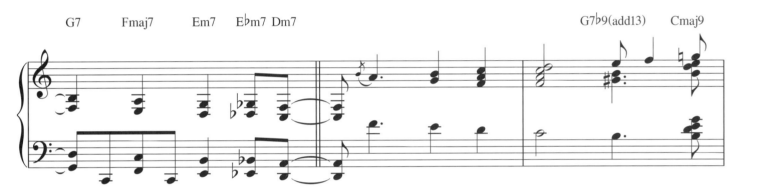

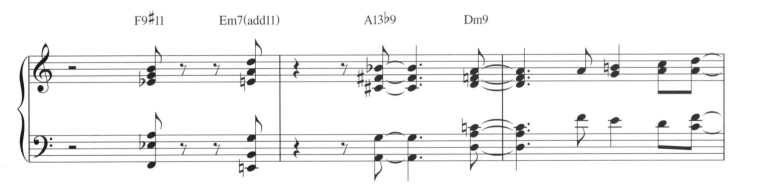

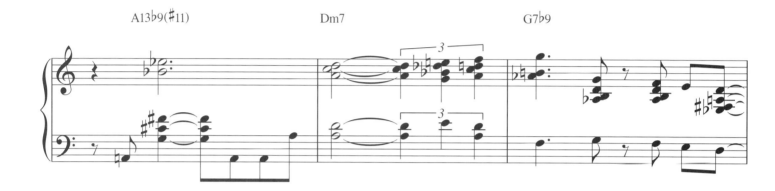

Em7   A(♭5)   Dm11   Dm9/G

E9   F9♭13   A13♭9   Dm

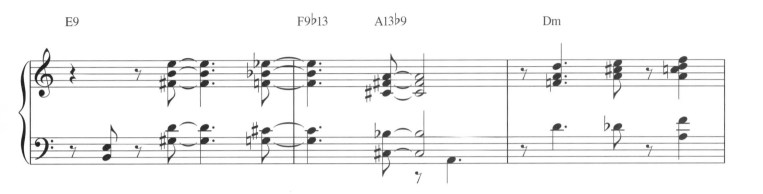

C6/G   D♭7#9   Cdim9

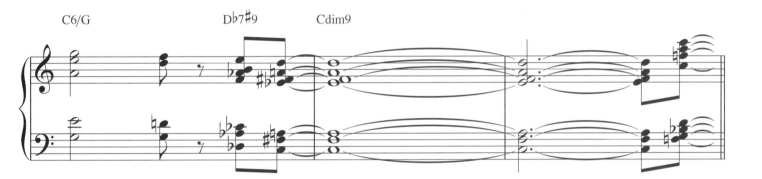

C13sus4   C9   C7♭9

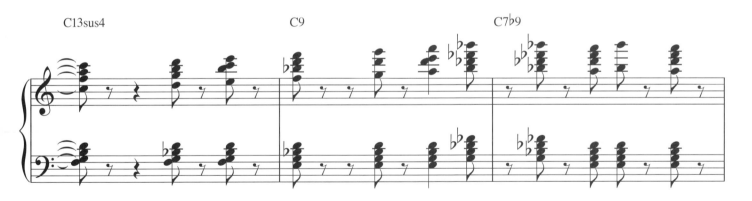

         Fmaj7   Em11   Gmaj7/A

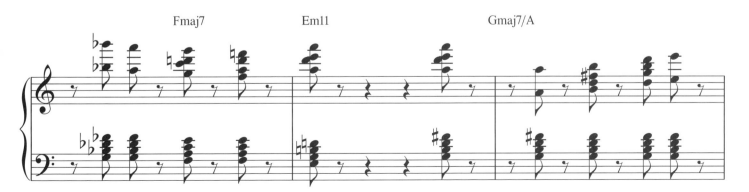

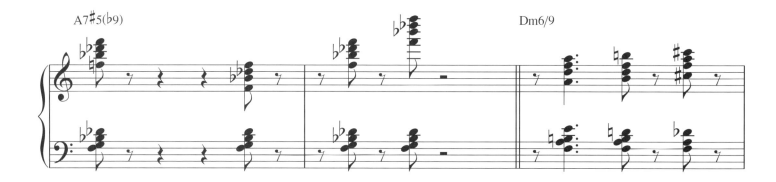

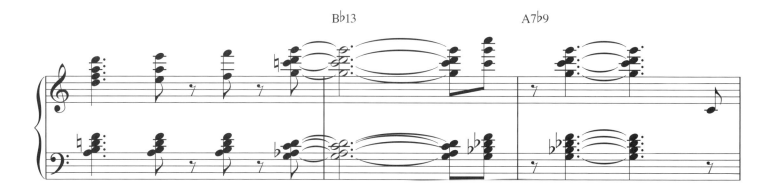

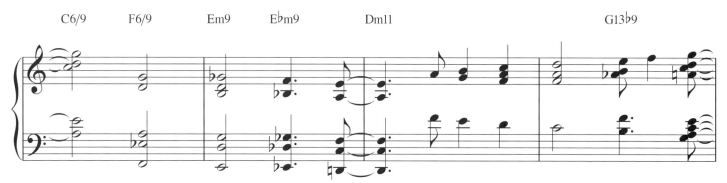

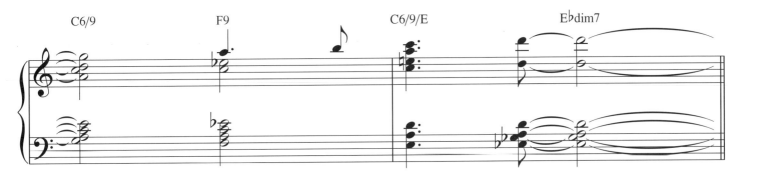

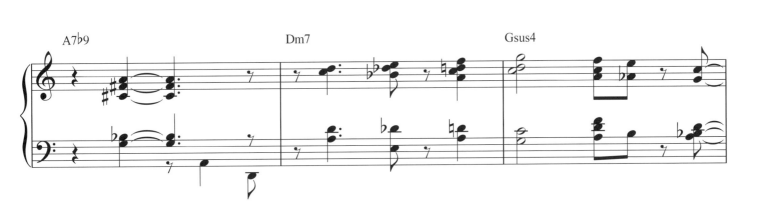

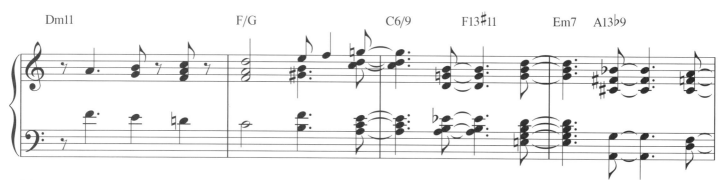

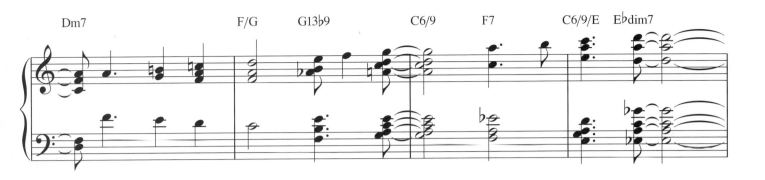

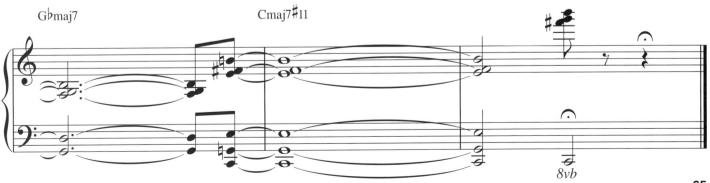

All of Me

Words and Music by Seymour Simons and Gerald Marks

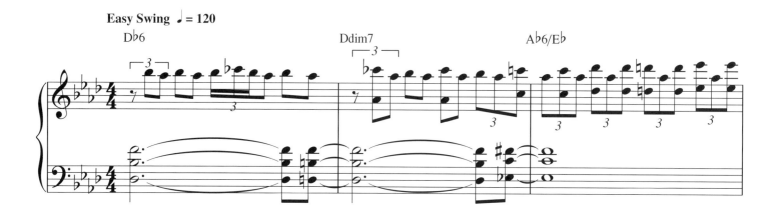

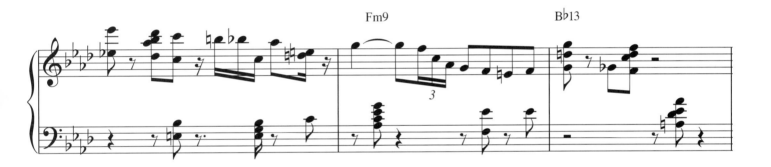

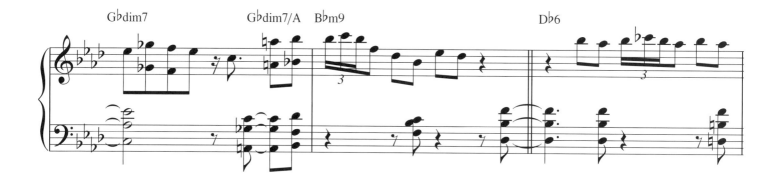

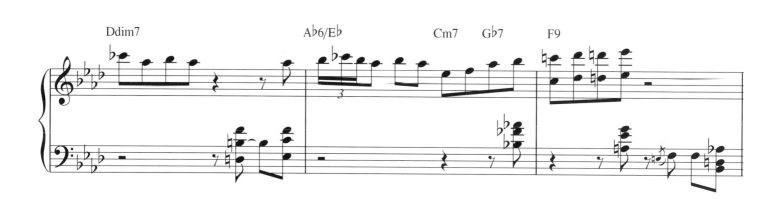

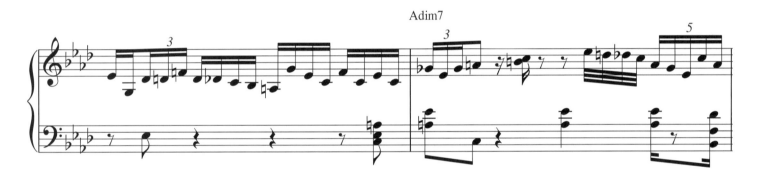

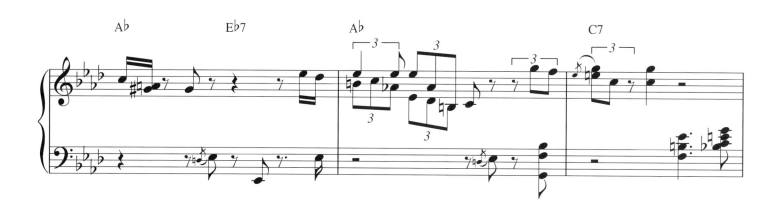

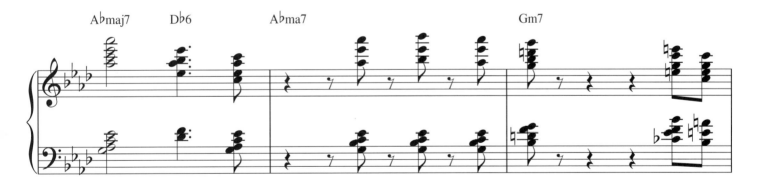

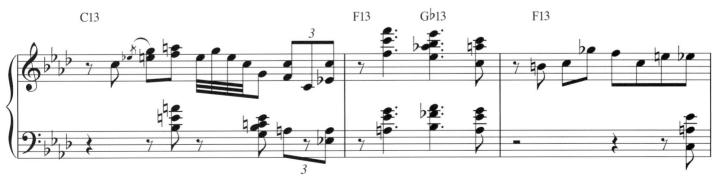

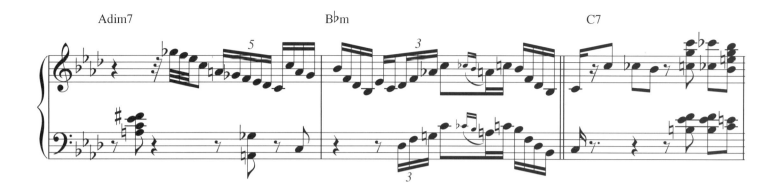

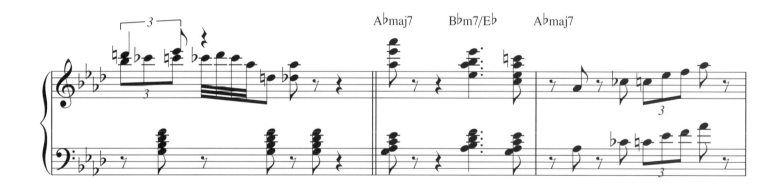

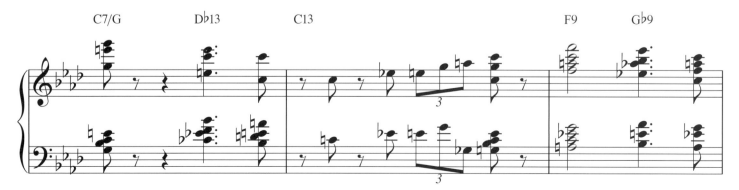

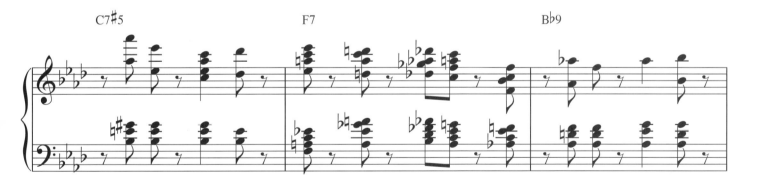

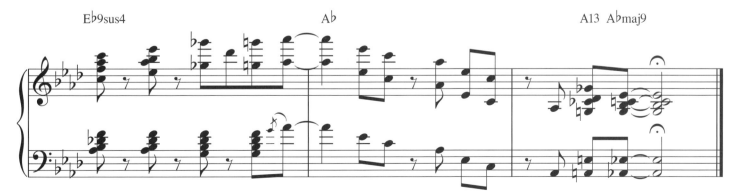

The Birth of the Blues

Words by B.G. DeSylva and Lew Brown
Music by Ray Henderson

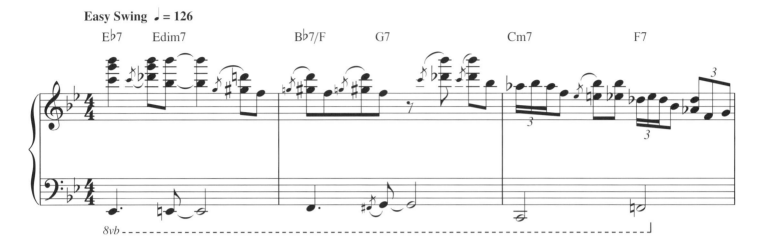

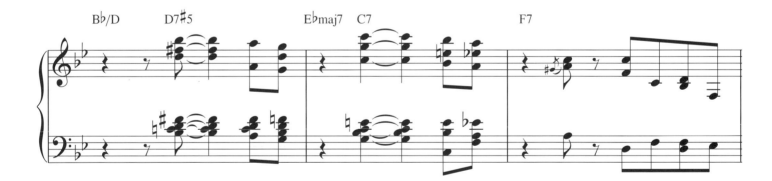

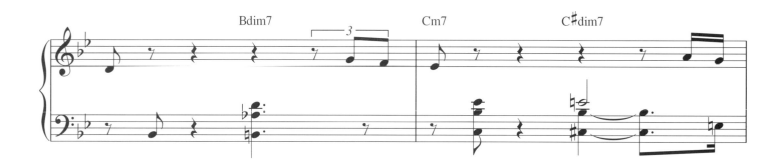

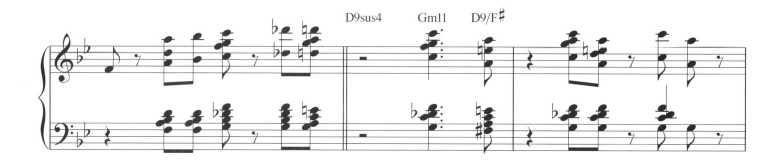

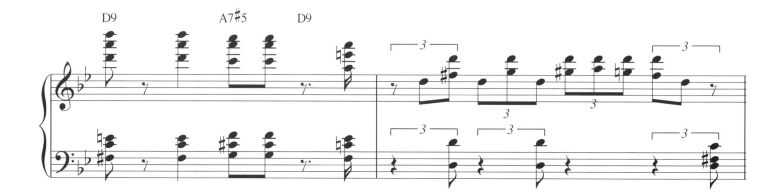

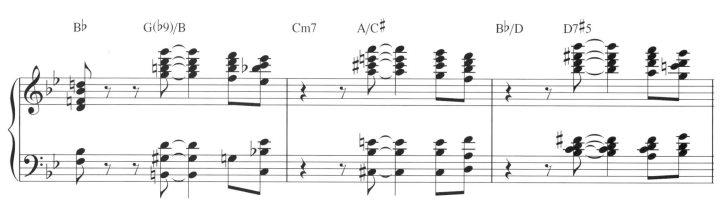

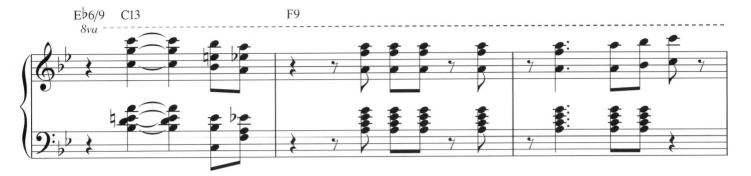

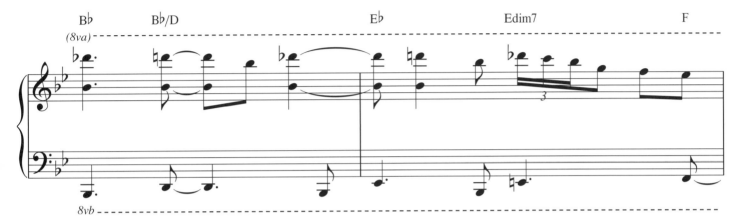

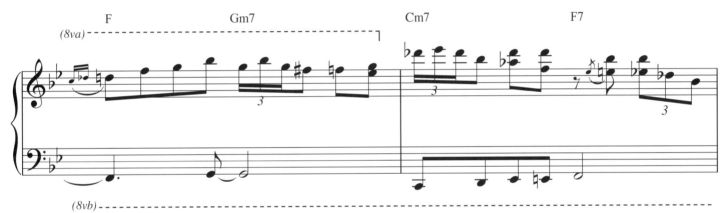

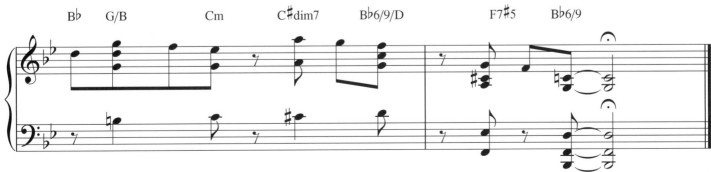

How About You?

Words by Ralph Freed
Music by Burton Lane

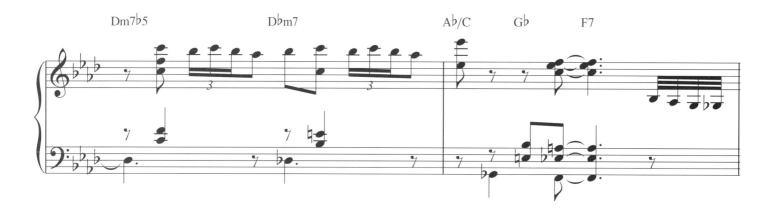

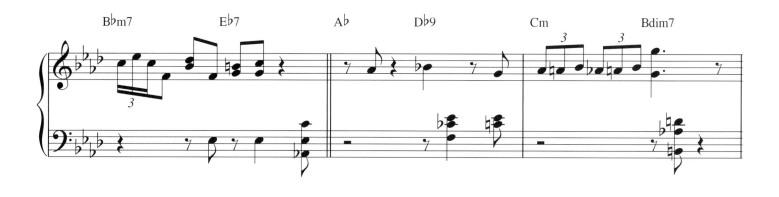

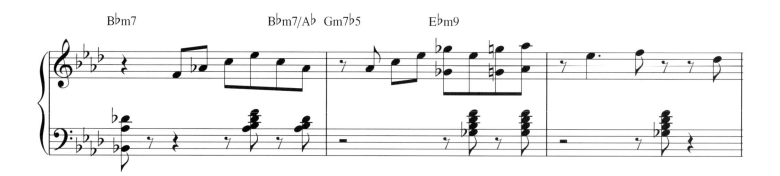

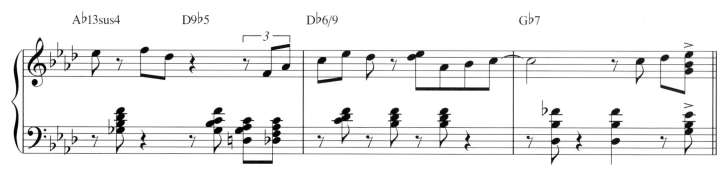

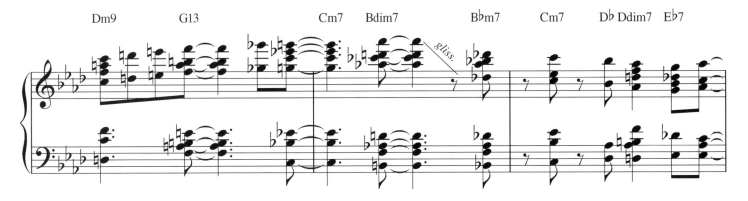

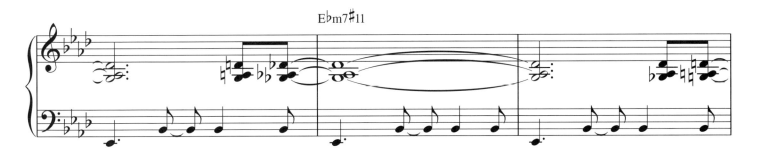

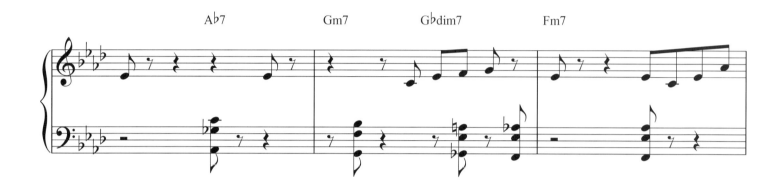

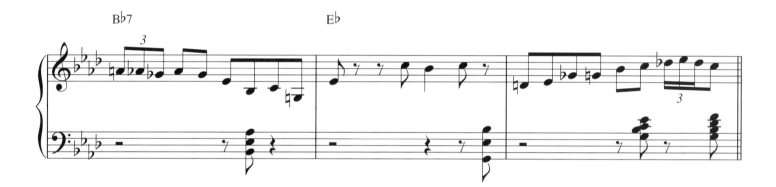

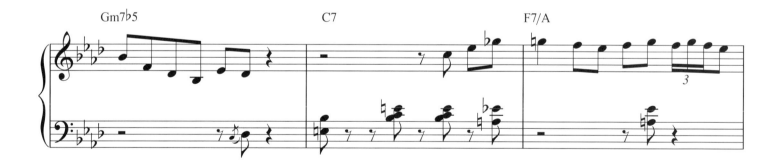

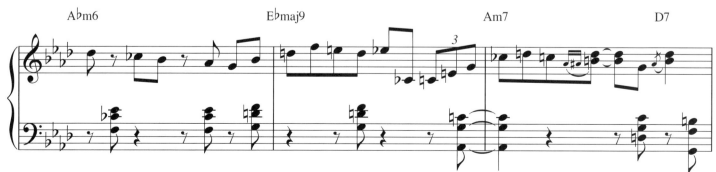

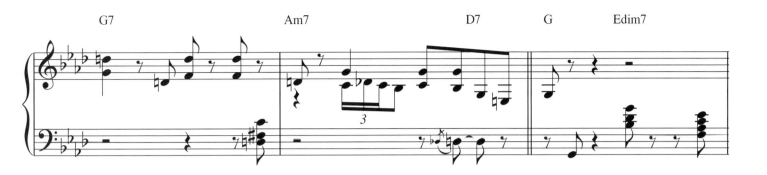

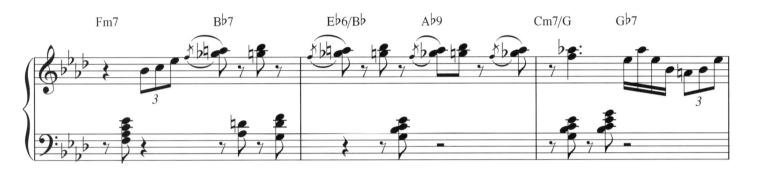

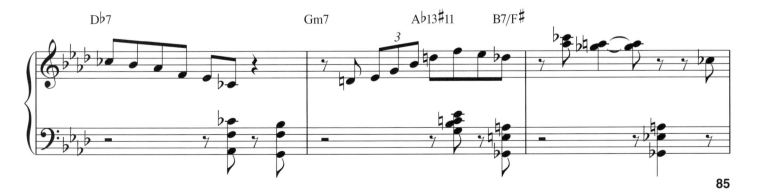

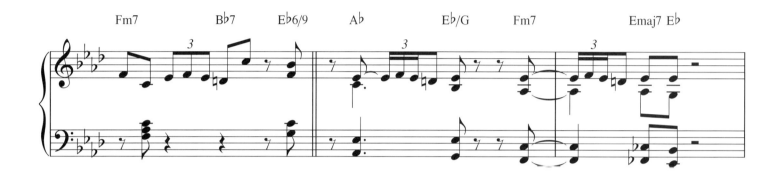

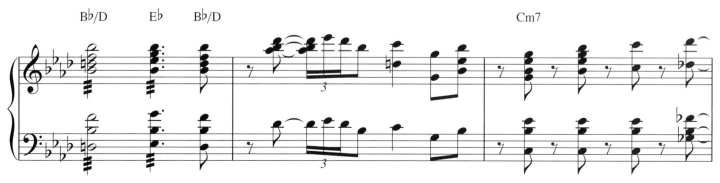

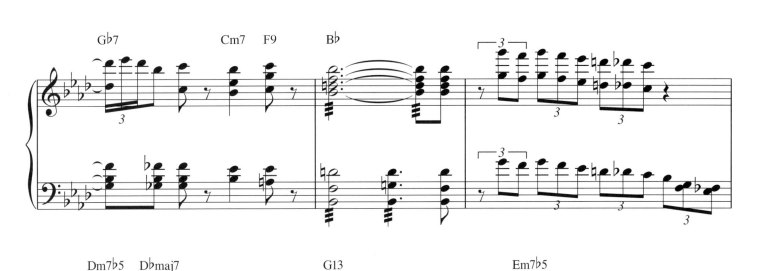

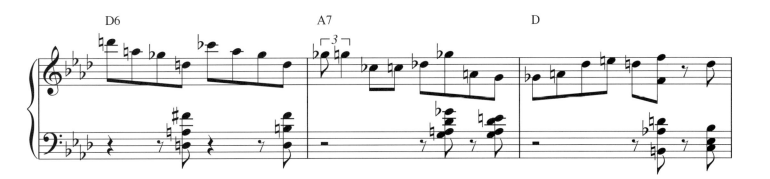

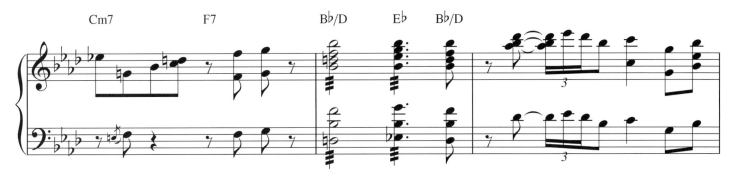

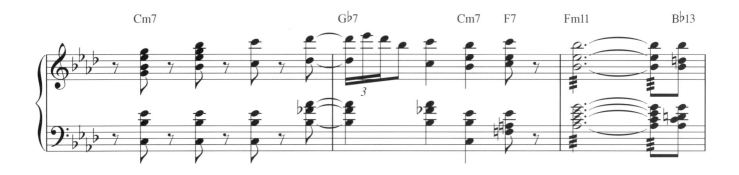

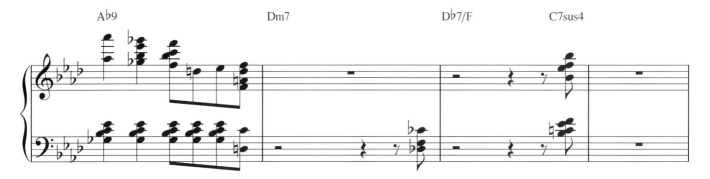

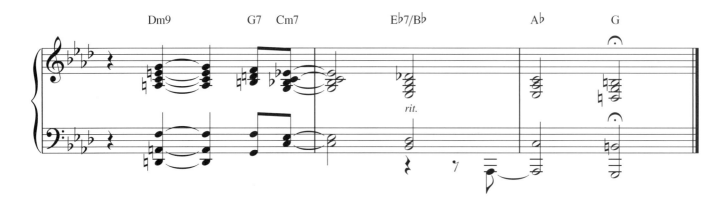